DEDICATED TO ALL THOSE WHO DREAM OF THE SEA!

DRAWN AND WRITTEN BY DAVE GARDNER
<DAVEGARDNERART.COM>

COLOR BY TENTIN GILLETTE

<u>THANK YOU!</u> STACY, BRIAN, ALEX, ROB, BUZZ, KIRIN!, GRADY, JANE, TESSA, JULIANE, ADRIANE, BOOGIE, MY FAMILY, MY NEIGHBORHOOD, THE WATER AND WAVES!
<u>THANKS</u> TO THE MUSIC OF ULAAN PASSERINE, DIRTY THREE, ALI AKHBAR KAHN, DEVO, JIMI HENDRIX, VELVET UNDERGROUND.
<u>THANKS</u> TO SURF INSPIRATIONS: RELL SUNN, GEORGE GREENOUGH, MIKE STEWART, MIKI DORA, JAY ADAMS, DAN TAYLOR, TERRY WADE, GERRY LOPEZ, BUTTONS AND ALL THE HAWAIIANS. RESPECT AND ALOHA!

Saltylittlesliders.com

SUNNY
KOA
FINN
MOON

THE ADVENTURES OF THE
SALTY LITTLE SLIDERS

DAVE
GARDNER

HOW DO
YOU
KNOW
YOUR
FRIENDS?
WHERE
DO
FRIENDS
COME
FROM?

WHY DOES THIS FEEL SO GOOD? HOW WAS YOUR FIRST SLIDE?

HOW FUN TO ENJOY AN-OTHERS' FUN?

WHO IS THAT FLYING BY? HOW DO YOU DO THAT? HOW CAN I DO THAT?

BETTER LATE THAN NEVER! SOMETIMES HEAD FIRST, SOMETIMES HEART FIRST...

HOW GOOD TO SHARE LUNCH!

WHAT ABOUT WHEN THERE ARE NO WAVES? NO PROB-LEM!!

DID YOU KNOW? YOU CAN FLY THROUGH CLOUDS UNDER THE SEA!

WHO ALREADY LIVES OUT THERE? HOW SHOULD WE BE AND BEHAVE AROUND THEM?

WHO GETS TO SEE LIFE PLAY FROM SO CLOSE?

WHO ELSE DO YOU WANT TO FLY LIKE?

WHO PUSHES THE TIDES? WHAT PULLS THE TIDES? HOW? WHY?

WHAT MAKES THE WAVES? HOW? WHY? WHAT ABOUT WHEN THERE ARE NO WAVES?

WHERE ARE THE INNER-MOST LIMITS OF PURE FUN?

HOW FUN TO RIDE TO-GETH-ER!

HOW GOOD TO ENJOY THE GIFTS OF THE SUN!

BOARD ENOUGH FOR ONE IS BOARD ENOUGH FOR TWO!

TO CELE-
BRATE EACH DAY.
TO CELE-
BRATE EACH OTHER.

HOW DO YOU KNOW WHEN TO GO?

OR NOT TO GO?

ARE THERE LIMITS TO WHAT YOU CAN DO? TO WHAT CAN BE DONE?

SOMETIMES ITS BETTER TO REGRET SOMETHING YOU HAVE DONE, RATHER THAN REGRET SOMETHING YOU HAVEN'T DONE...

GO FAST. DON'T RUSH.

TO
GLIDE
AND TO
SLIDE
WITH
GRACE
UNDER
PRESSURE

THERE IS ALWAYS A WAY....

DO YOU DREAM OF WAVES IN OTHER WAYS?

REST.
GIVE THANKS.
DREAM.
LOOK FOR-WARD TO TOM-ORROW.
REPEAT.

IS THE BEACH THE BEGIN-NING OF THE SEA OR THE END OF THE LAND? WHY ARE WE SO DRAWN TO THE WAVES?

A BEGINNING......

CPSIA information can be obtained at www.ICGtesting.com
Printed in the USA
LVIW01n0900301017
553794LV00005B/9